Bog Cotton

haiku stories & haiku

Ken Jones

Alba Publishing

Published by Alba Publishing
P O Box 266, Uxbridge
UB9 5NX, United Kingdom
www.albapublishing.com

A catalogue record for this book is available from the British Library

ISBN: 978-0-9572592-2-5

Edited, designed and typeset by Kim Richardson
Cover image © Ken Crossan
Printed by Ashford Colour Press

10 9 8 7 6 5 4 3 2 1

Acknowledgments

Grateful acknowledgement is due to the editors of *Blithe Spirit, Haiku Presence, Modern Haiku, Frogpond, Haibun Today*, and *Contemporary Haibun Online* in which magazines most of these haibun and haiku first appeared.

I am grateful to David Cobb, and to George Marsh, Jim Norton and other members of the HaikuProse Group for their helpful comments, without which this book would have been the poorer. My thanks are also due to my wife, Noragh, who was the first to sample each draft.

The support and encouragement of journal editors Colin Blundell, Jim Kacian, and Jeffrey Woodward has, over the years, been more valuable to me than perhaps they know. Finally, working with Kim Richardson of Alba Publishing, with its high design standards, has been a great pleasure.

Contents

Foreword   6

Preface   8

Black Comedy   9

  Followers of the Great Way   *10*

  Laughing Gas   *11*

  Dying in Luxury   *13*

  Making it to Twenty-Ten   *15*

  Le Chef Propose   *16*

  The Blue Moon Café   *18*

  Witches White and Black   *20*

  Haiku   *22*

Out on the Hill   25

  A Plodding Present   *26*

  A Waterlogged Dream   *27*

  Dreams Wander On   *28*

  On the Sharp Edge of Nowhere   *29*

  Broken Shotguns   *32*

  Seven Pieces of Silver   *33*

  Haiku   *35*

Sauntering   37

  The Long Passage   *38*

  Things to See and Do   *40*

  Tram Fever   *41*

  Haiku   *43*

Love and Lust   45
   An End To It   46
   Master John Goodfellow and the Velveteen Mouse Trap   46
   A Season out of Mind   48
   Leonora   50
   The Ascent   52
   The Path   53
   Haiku   54

Things Aren't What They Seem   57
   Insentient Beings   58
   Satisfaction Guaranteed   59
   Alter Ego   60
   Deconstruction   61
   Colophon   63
   Haiku   64

A Life   67
   Afternoon at the Biographicum   68
   Out on the Knocker   69
   Gift of the Gab   71
   La Vie en Rose   73
   Sibelius and I   74
   Appointment with Yama   77
   The Brass Name Plate   78
   Haiku   80

The Grave and Constant   83
   Honour and Glory   84
   Love and Silence   86
   The Fall   87

The Lost and the Found   88

The Dying   89

Stone Age   90

Bog Cotton   91

Haiku   93

Foreword

Once upon a time, not so terribly long ago, I read a story about a gentleman who regaled a lady, over a glass of fine wine, with revelations of his life as a hermit. Many, upon a first glance, would judge that approach a decidedly risky amorous stratagem. Ken Jones, in an early and ambitious book, told this tale about his own person. Whether it is bare fact or an embellishment of truth in the interest of cunning fiction, this anecdote registers with me now, as it did then, as an accurate portrait of the man that I've come to know via his generous, personal correspondence and my own study, over many seasons, of his haiku and haibun.

Ken Jones, indeed, may share something of the hermit's reluctance to converse idly or at length and may share the hermit's pleasure in a quiet retreat but he, like the suave fellow who deftly pours another glass for his charmed lady, is likewise urbane and well-acquainted with the complex and contradictory claims of the modern world. He is a writer of incisive wit who, in his often gentle and good-natured sketches of our all-too-human failings, rarely neglects to lampoon his own shortcomings and obsessions as well.

Readers of *Bog Cotton* will be impressed by the range of its subject matter. They will encounter stories of affairs brought to an end and of would-be affairs without beginning; tales of everyday objects, such as toasters, tea kettles or water taps, that assume lives of their own; matter-of-fact relations of seafaring witches who suddenly occupy an unsuspecting harbor village and of hand puppets that enact the marital discord of their makers. Many works in this volume parallel the novel of manners; their settings, indicative of their shifting focus upon social class and custom, vary greatly: a hospital operating theater, a workingman's coffee house, a modernist art gallery, a rustic hunting party or a ferry to an uninhabited island. Travels abroad to Antwerp or Dublin enliven certain of these tales but, more often than not, the terrain that haunts our author is a short walk away, in the Welsh countryside that he calls home, where the tragic history of

Wales is reflected in "a landscape rich only in names" and populated by "locals struggling to make English sense of their lost language."

Variety may attract the impartial reader but breadth alone isn't sufficient to secure his or her abiding interest. Ken Jones must be commended, also, for the depth of his achievement in mastering difficult motifs with his concise but allusive and figurative style. Those qualities define his haiku and his stories alike. His voice, deliberately measured and nuanced, relies upon paradox, black humor, irony and ambiguity to create an understated but multifaceted text that invites his reader's full participation. He, in prefaces to past collections, places repeated emphasis upon his writing as entertainment; his ideal reader, nevertheless, does not view the text as simple recreation but, in answering the poet's call, conceives of it, instead, as a space for frequent *re-creation*.

Haibun in English—or the "haiku story," as Ken Jones would have it —has become, albeit largely underground in reputation, an expansive, international and labyrinthine literature. The truly exceptional writers in this genre are few in number. Ken Jones must be counted among that precious company. His pioneering presence has been constant for fifteen or more years. I have turned the pages of *Bog Cotton*, therefore, with the delight and anticipation that led me through five previous titles by this Welsh poet. He has yet to disappoint me.

Jeffrey Woodward
Detroit
31 August 2012

Preface

Dear Reader,

The haiku here can speak for themselves. The prose pieces ("haibun") are written in a haiku style and include haiku designed to dance with the prose and give it an added flavour. Originating in seventeenth century Japan they are now, in the West, a novel literary genre with an exciting range of possibilities. In this book their affinity is, for the most part, with the short story.

The material is arranged under topics, in seven sections, to welcome in the browser in a playful spirit of curiosity. It resembles the different flavours pictured on a box of chocolates, to be savoured at leisure. Each section contains both haibun and freestandng haiku to follow.

At public readings I am usually asked how much truth there is in a particular story. Some of the haibun are clearly more fictional than others. However, all are "truthlike" in that they are grounded in my own experience, however much they may be imaginatively enhanced.

Ken Jones, Cwm Rheidol, November 2012

BLACK COMEDY

Followers of the Great Way

Swaying above the summer bracken the great scarlet banner proclaims... well, er... something or other. A brawny probation officer bears it aloft at the head of our little procession. The din we make scatters to the ten directions all uneasy spirits.

> PowerPoint
> the chief executive
> blasts the thigh-bone trumpet

> > Unemployed
> > she clashes
> > the brass cymbals

> The divorcée
> croons a mantra
> to soothe the Hungry Ghosts

> > A wrathful deity
> > wears the mask
> > of a loss adjuster

We circle round the stupa, raised on the banks of a stream. Anima and animus—running water and resistant rock. Clockwise, of course. Lest we unravel the universe. Through clouds of incense flames leap from a rusty bucket atop the cairn. Each of us bows, and adds our stone. Midge cream we offer to the Angry Ghosts.

Then, on yellow fertiliser bags, we sit with our minds.

> Meditation
> the stillness of the stream
> flowing through our brains

However, the unreconstructed loss adjustor does a visualisation of the divorcee as a *dakini*, bare-breasted and dancing wildly in her girdle of skulls.

And so, back to the meditation hall, where once again we try to figure out who we are.

~ ~ ~ ~ ~ ~

Laughing Gas

> Pastel colours and faint smiles
> from face to face
> we size each other up

Thankfully all turn out to be "people like us". Gathered here in the Small Function Room we are welcomed to the Graceful Exit workshop. Tea and biscuits thaw us out.

> Trainee suicide
> her sweet smile
> "Just one lump, please"

The Instructor comes breezing in, bearing a reused IKEA packing case, across which some wag has scribbled "Pluto" with a black marker. "I've just got to settle up with the hotel", he says. "See if you can put this together. But don't try it out to see if it works. We're not insured, and I don't want any of you to hear the trumpets sounding on the other side. Not yet, anyway."

The blokes fall upon the box with all their usual competitive banter, to which the women are resigned. All, that is, except Gerald—an earnest and rather anxious young man.

> In shaky italic
> on ruled feint
> how to kill himself
> properly

In no time the plastic bags and hoses, the cylinder and all the smaller bits and pieces have been assembled into an elegant helium gas suicide machine. All but fifty brightly-coloured party balloons which are supposed to be inflated with the cylinder. For some celebratory occasion.

The women amuse themselves by blowing up the balloons. Diana gets a gulp of the heady helium and breaks into falsetto mirth. Ignoring all this brittle playfulness the Instructor delivers a lucid talk, with a bit of black comedy here and there. Clearly he could take his own life umpteen times without a single false move.

> On the cylinder
> the feeble flutter
> of a winter butterfly

Finally, he draws our attention to a recent news item. In a hotel bedroom a German businessman—*Vorsprung durch Technik*—had efficiently done away with himself using only a modest amount of helium. This anecdote is intended to reassure us. But for the first time that day the Small Function Room falls silent.

> The person *gone*
> what remains
> in a well-pressed suit

At the farewells I congratulate the Instructor on his mastery of DIY extinction. There's only one thing missing. Ourselves.

> Through a shower of yellow leaves
> my veined hands
> tight on the wheel

[Pluto – Lord of the Underworld.]
[*Vorsprung durch technik* – "Progress through technology".]

Dying in Luxury

> Waiting to be ticked
> that last little box
> "Deceased"

On all the doors the pattern of veneer is identical. The décor is in an analgesic pastel shade. On my wall is the badly painted picture of an old wheelbarrow, from which droop gaily painted flowers. Had they known what might happen, they would have decorated the passenger saloons of the "Titanic" thus.

> Through each half-open door
> the stillness of a life
> half-closed

For those of us who are up to it, the event of the day is the morning *passeggiata*, back and forth along the thickly carpeted corridor. Everybody has tried to make the best of themselves. "Must keep up standards, you know".

> Urine cathetered
> her Gucci handbag
> a rich Sauternes

With a debonair twist of my own piss bag I offer her a flirty smile. And here's a patrician gent, with his shock of white hair, well-cut dressing gown and creased pyjama bottoms.

> Lord of the Universe
> with each faltering step
> his firmly planted Zimmer frame

Shortly after I arrive, my surgeon, Dr Pangloss, invites me to accompany him on a voyage round my urinary system. A couple of specialist nurses join us for the trip—they have already seen countless dicks, all hors de combat. With the aid of a minute telescopic television camera we cruise up my urethra, caught on the big screen with Pangloss's running commentary. The stalactites are impressive. Getting past the prostate proves to be a tight squeeze. The nurses stifle a giggle. "Partial demolition tomorrow", promises the surgeon. Then we're out into the roomy cavern of my bladder. The walls are a not unpleasing red, apparently the result of a radiotherapy blowlamp job several years ago.

> Mortal inside
> my own insides
> so this is what I am?

Later, I comment to the Ward Sister on the cheerful eccentricities of the nursing staff—and, indeed, everyone else. She attributes this to the generous staffing policy, from consultants to cleaners. "Here, in the private sector, we each have enough time to go mad in our own individual ways, whereas in the NHS everyone grows mad in much the same way. So, put on that risqué bare-backed gown, my dear, and we'll whisk you off now to the live theatah." Here I get into an argument with the anaesthetist about the Latin tag *Et in Arcadia ego*. Knowing that, given a couple of minutes, he's bound to get in the last word. Which he does. Et in Arcadia ego…

> *Strictly Come Dancing*
> the Reaper and I
> take a tentative turn

[*Et in Arcadia ego*. Loosely translatable as "Death dwells even in Arcadia"—even in the blissful unconsciousness of anaesthesia. Hence a timely warning to the anaesthetist, and the "tentative turn".]

~ ~ ~ ~ ~

Making it to Twenty-Ten

> A weary man
> lost in thought
> an aged butterfly
> between his thighs   *Nagata Koi*

"A pagan Christian", she confesses. Chunky Celtic jewellery. Earrings that dingle-dangle. A long purple skirt and a brightly coloured top. What estate agents call "a well presented property". Limited liability retail flirts—she and I.

> The room warms up
> a winter butterfly
> all a-flutter

So, the four of us have actually made it to the here and now. Miscellaneous surgical scars; repair jobs here and there; irreplaceable parts wearing out; one sort of pain or another. The 1930s not quite lost in history. But of course, no one here feels old.

> Two couples
> each of the four
> their own uneasy chair

Tossing her well-coiffed black hair, she fronts an animated discussion to do with Mary Magdalene. We each have our own agenda—well known to the other three after all those years. I chuck another log into the stove.

> "Whore or virgin?"
> on the stem of her glass
> her fingers play

My wife disagrees. Enjoying himself, her husband waves one foot in the air and sucks on his empty pipe. Stirring the pot I play the innocent.

To mellow the mood we break open the Leffe Abbey Belgian beer. "Roasted barley malt gives the beer its deep brown colour and fantastic combination of sweet caramel yet bitter taste." A Georges Brassens disk *La Chasse aux Papillons* ("The Butterfly Hunt"), and everyone begins to luxuriate.

Swilling the remains of our beer in the bottom of the glass, we round off the evening with a sing-song. Mal Pope's Swansea syncopation of "Bread of Heaven". *Guide me O thou great Jehovah, pilgrim through this barren land...*

In the porch light, her husband's silver quiff. And his firm handshake.

> Her good-night hug
> no longer
> no closer
> than it needs to be

[Nagata Koi (1900-1997): outstanding Zen haiku poet of old age. Translation by Margaret Mitsutani and Naruto Nana.]

~ ~ ~ ~ ~ ~

Le Chef Propose
With acknowledgement to Thomas Love Peacock

> Empty boats
> their lift and fall
> on the ocean swell

Absolute strangers. Politely we size each other up. By their apéritifs shall ye know them. In the middle of the rococo drawing room Hector holds forth, flourishing his pint of bitter. Hector "travels". In heavy machinery. His anxious wife clutches her gin and tonic. We talk about how we got here. Two of the men boast about their global positioning, "It all boils down to how you crossed the Jurassic fault", interrupts Rudolph, in the measured tones of academe. "Ah, indeed, but how did we get here?" chuckles Mary, a large, jolly woman, twirling the stem of her Tom Collins.

Reverend Mary Magdalene
her cleavage
divides the parish

"Starters are more to the point", mutters the Head of Social Services, waving the menu, "who's for the Vine Tomato Soup and who's for the Savoyard Platter?" Then it's Who's Holidayed Where—a competitive bored game. However, the wine list offers a challenge of interpersonal footwork and pure bluff, somehow avoiding a power struggle among the men.

Spoiling the flavour
each self
taken out to dine

Enter the chef, in a tall, starched hat. With a flourish he lifts each lid in turn, to "ahs!" and "ohs!" of appreciation. From each tureen there rises a cloud of steam. As the party mellows I lament the fate of helpless comestibles:

Wrapped in cellophane
baby shitake mushrooms
ah! the sadness!

"Indeed! How can we avoid evil?" exclaims the Reverend Mary, stabbing her ossobuco through its gremolata topping. "Not my field, really", mutters Rudolph, delving with the zeal of a geologist into his Gratin Dauphinois.

Conversation
the awkward gap
becomes a perilous silence

Mercifully this is filled by the necessity of choice, between *Light & Dark Chocolate Tiramasu with Kahlia Coffee Liqueur OR Strawberry & Cream Gateau with Grand Marnier.*

And so to the lounge, for *Coffee with Belgian Truffles*. I am emboldened by my warming *digestivo*: "My friends, have we not demonstrated that the human condition is essentially paranoiac?" But by now this evokes no more response than the pastoral scenes embossed on the wallpaper. "Just as you say, old chap"; Hector humours me with a clap on the back.

> In and out of the scudding clouds
> talking moonshine
> The Man in the Moon

~ ~ ~ ~ ~ ~

The Blue Moon Café

"Beef tagine, with couscous and hot crusty bread - £6.50
Chicken & vegetable pie, served with salad - £6.50
Broccoli, stilton & chestnut tartlet - £6.00"

But after a glance through the window, most passers-by move on. Each table is occupied by a solitary diner. Perhaps, like me, refugees from those little corner tables in places bright and bustling with couples and parties. Here there is only the clink of cutlery, murmured orders, the well-bred clearing of a throat, and the occasional ching of the till and scrape of a chair.

> "Will it be solitude
> or loneliness
> this evening, sir?"

Most of the diners are elderly men. Some try to keep up appearances —tight-lipped, with the straight back and clipped moustache. Maybe, on the way out, the once jaunty tilt of the homburg of a man-about-town. Most no longer try.

Lodging house
the stem of his pipe
half bitten through

A newcomer, hungry for company, blunders in. Hail fellow, well-met. Tries to engage the old gent at the next table, who is surely a retired undertaker. "Merchant navy, y'know; seen a bit o' the world. I tell you, this country's gone to the dogs." The whole place freezes. Even the café cat darts into the kitchen. "How interesting", murmurs the old gent, blowing on his carrot and coriander soup and making it quite clear that it isn't.

At the table next to mine is the kind of older woman who is the romantic staple of my evenings as a commercial traveller. Between courses I let my imagination out to play. Then hazard a cautious flicker of the eye lashes, the hint of a smile, the slightest raising of the eyebrows. Alas! Clamping shut her privacy she opens her book and smoothes it *flat*.

All hope evaporates of an erotically-laced chat over coffee on unreliable narratives in the contemporary novel. My only consolation is a glance at the cover when she leaves. No, it isn't a Camus. Only some bodice-ripping chick-lit.

"'The Edward Hopper Calendar'—what a good choice !" I exclaim to the proprietress, glancing at the wall above the till. With my change, no words but a certain smile.

"One New Year's evening", one of my customers in the town tells me later, "Josephine rearranged the chairs around a single large table, decorating it with candles and flowers. The response was disastrous. She nearly went bust." He adds, with a chuckle, "her mistake was to use real flowers."

Deftly she whisks away the other setting
serving solitude
with the soup

Witches White and Black

> Red Sand Bay
> even the devouring tides
> can never scour it clean

Dyed by some folk memory of a Viking massacre. Above, wild ponies graze the glowering hill fort of Arthur's Table. Huddled uneasily between the two—bewitched Llanddona.

In those far off days before the Great War there came a young geology student, attracted by the fossil-rich limestone of that place. He was surprised that there was no inn in such a large village; was it the grip of Calvinistic Methodism, tight even for that time and place? No one would speak to him, not even to laugh at his sort of Welsh. He never forgot that flicker of fear behind their eyes. So it was beside the salt marshes that he pitched his tent.

It was here that a white witch became his strange and graceful lover. And always beneath a rowan tree

> In passion's heat
> drawn by the semen scent
> the dance of gilded flies

Lilith was her name—after the alternative Eve. She had come to lift the curse off the village.

Some two hundred years earlier, a mysterious boat full of witches and warlocks had drifted into the bay.

> Grinding on sand
> an oarless keel
> on the falling tide

The witches put a curse on the terrified villagers, who had tried to push them out to sea again. And they set up their own black magic community from which they terrorised the people of Llanddona. There was Siân Bwt, only four feet tall, and with two thumbs on her left hand to mark her as an authentic witch. And most feared of all was Bela Fawr, who could turn herself into a hare and suck dry the cow of any villager who would not do her bidding. And if anyone were to cross the menfolk they would be blinded by the black flies harboured in their neckchiefs.

> In a dark wind
> night after night
> the pines mutter and screech

Such is the story my grandfather confided in me before he died. Locked in my desk is the black crane bag Lilith had given him. Inside, seven fox's teeth. I wish now I hadn't opened it… Visiting Llanddona it seems that the curse has indeed been lifted. The friendly place now has a pub, named after our shape-shifting national hero Owain Glyndwr. The publican tells me there are "three self-advertised white witches on the housing estate". Lilith's daughters perhaps, still keeping a benign eye on things?

> Across moonlit sands
> a vixen's cry
> deep-throated silence

~ ~ ~ ~ ~ ~

Haiku

In full dress uniform
a Greater Spotted Woodpecker
disperses the bird bath mob

Gamma male
the waitress serves me
last

Dark strangers
wing mirrors
clash by night

Narrow lane
the passing
of a non-returnable smile

The old pot-holer
tells me about
his world-historical stance

My spade and her rake
together in moonlight
what a pair!

Pulling the cracker
my left hand and my right hand
enjoy Christmas together

Octogenarian wheelbarrow
the wheel replacement
a major operation

Chiselling the last digit
on his memorial
trouble with serifs

Lingering at the passing place
the train falls silent
the passengers are blessed

Behind the curtain
a tumble of teddies
gathering dust

We three unsteady friends
raising our glasses
to the morning star

OUT ON THE HILL

A Plodding Present

Beyond the ruin a gap-toothed fence of upright slates. And a green track. Leaving the pasture it climbs steadily through scrub and heather, wild and lonely. I follow unseen black beasts, their hoof prints filled with thin Welsh rain. Each time they disappear into a bog finding the way on the other side becomes more difficult. Finally no more than a sheep path through dead bracken, round outcrops blotched with ghostly lichens. I hide inside my hood from a flurry of hailstones boxing my ears.

The raw landscape becomes more intimate. This bleak solitude thins me out. And what's left is edged with frisson.

> a broken ankle
> and a sharp young moon
> playing hide-and-seek

But, for now, the ground levels off, the wind grows keener, and the path and I finally lose ourselves in a confusion of bogs, pools and hillocks. The broad back of the pass. Over on the right is what must be Pen Carreg Gopa. It's somehow reassuring to be able to put a name to a face—even one which has so little to say.

Ahead the land falls away and, in fading light, a panorama of waterlogged tussocks, stretching away to the horizon—pathless and impassable. Spreading my map on a rock I bite into a Crunchie bar

Half a mile to the left a great conifer blanket covers the moor. Ten thousand tight-packed sitka spruce—a sterile no-man's-land. Except for the open mouth of a firebreak, reaching to a distant logging road. Or perhaps not? I let it swallow me up. Dipping and rising, it soon shuts out the moor behind, while far ahead the dark green tunnel fills with evening mist.

> The plodding present
> a firebreak
> through a forest without end

A Waterlogged Dream

> Jagged and buckled
> by too many winters
> the once-smooth tarmac

I abandon the car and trudge on through the forestry to the end of the broken road. Ahead rises a pedestrian nightmare. To the mountaineer a very modest massif. But so many ups and downs, bogs and tussocks, and neither paths nor tracks of man nor beast. Cresting each skyline, another skyline. Drunken, the compass needle reels this way and that.

Mercifully, at last I stumble upon the dried-up remains of a leat, which once watered the dreams of some distant mine captain. Along and round the hillsides it winds. On the map, a falsely blue umbilical thread, leading to the source.

> On the frozen lake
> my apple core
> rests on its own reflection

If you will, in pyjamas or stout boots, you too might visit this waterlogged dream. Climb northings 269950; veer 278700 eastings. There you will find the concrete obelisk, 1957 feet, hugged by a drystone wall. *Llan Ddu Fawr*—the "Big Black Enclosure"—is what Yr Hen Bobl, "The People Before Time", called this stony dream.

And, at journey's end, you will come upon a grey stone bothy resting in a fold of the hills. Here, in dusty silence, everything lies waiting.

> Candle grease
> on the Visitors' Book
> the biro's blank scratches

[*Yr Hen Bobl* (Welsh): lit. "The Old People"]
[Bothy: a simple unlocked cottage for hill walkers]

Dreams Wander On

> Window filled with drifting cloud
> Earth turns
> the day hangs in the air

On the patterned tablecloth the patterned map. A wild, rolling upland, reinforced with sellotape along the folds. The scarcely inhabited parishes of Llanddewi Abergwesyn and Llanfihangel Abergwesyn—I roll them round my mouth. My boots replaced with a magnifying glass and my imagination freed by confinement, I can cross both parishes between sips of coffee.

With a forefinger several hundred yards wide I push my way through dense green rectangles of sitka spruce. I follow my past along the pecked red lines of paths and bridleways, pausing at reminders in fading biro: arrows, crosses, ticks, question and exclamation marks.

> Old age enjoyed
> "be-wilder-ment"
> that tangled, wild-eyed word

A landscape rich only in place names, spread everywhere across the wriggling orange contours. Placeless place names, useful only to the long dead locals. The familiar Welsh of hill and pasture, stream and woodland, repeated over and over again. But now and again my wandering eyeglass pauses. Ty Harlot—some bucolic brothel ? And Ty Sais—the Englishman's House.

> Broken ribbed house
> its staring windows
> in the western light

Here's Moelprysgau, where I've passed many a haunted night. A sour, boggy place. Its broken fences wander aimlessly through the yellow grass, before losing themselves in blanket spruce. At least four recorded murders hereabouts, three by Evan Edwards. Stabbed his pregnant wife near Pen Bwlch Rhyd y Meirch. She'd discovered he was keeping a mistress down at Pontrhydfendigaid—"The-Bridge-at-the-Ford of-the-Blessed-Virgin".

Rising wind
the moonlit pines
mutter and screech

And yet... the great Revivals... those singing bands of men and women striding with their lanterns across my map. *"Guide us O thou great Jehovah, pilgrim though this barren land."*

This map once framed *"an original race... who had cultivated their own individuality from generation to generation without let or hindrance, and where every man, woman and child was an entirely new edition of humanity."*

Remains of the day
all the potholes
filled with silver

[The (unattributed) end quotation is from Ruth Bidgood's *Parishes of the Buzzard* (Goldleaf, 2000), p197. I am grateful to her for the background material used in this haibun.]

~ ~ ~ ~ ~

On the Sharp Edge of Nowhere

A flavoursome landscape. I linger too long on the ridge, recklessly sitting in the stone Fowler's Seat, opposite the Fowler's Horse Block, with a prehistoric circle between us. Slowly I pick my way down through a maze of bilious brown bogs, a bilious brown colouring on my map proclaiming my Right to Roam.

Legislation
made null and void
by bog and tussock.

Nightfall now, and grateful to stumble out upon a skinny crossroads, feeling the hard top under my boots. Exhausted, I sink down against the only ready building.

Facing David's Well
where warriors washed their wounds
a red phone box

In the murmuring stream I hear their lamentations still. Broken men, fleeing the disaster at Cilmeri where, on 11 December 1282, Llywelyn the Last, prince of Wales, was slain and independence extinguished for some eight hundred years. Needless to say, the waters of the spring on every anniversary are tainted with their blood. For this is a land which holds myth and memory well.

Most of the dwellings sit uneasily in this raw landscape, which bares its scars so openly.

Heavy machinery
deep frozen ruts
in sun-baked clay

Even the Welsh language has died out here, in mysterious circumstances in the eighteenth century. Some of the English place names have a devil-may-care ring about them. Names like Moelfre City and the adjacent City Shop have a Wild West, or at least an urban feel, but turn out to be no more than a few straggling hill farms. In the middle of a forest, where a narrow tarred road finally gives up, Red Lion lies beside a lily pond. Corrupted I'm told, from Rhyd Lleian—the Nun's Ford—by locals struggling to make English sense of their lost language. Still deeper in the forest an empty house stares back blankly, each window blinded by the national flag. Five faded dragons.

A nowhere place, this land is open to eccentric visionaries whom it speedily swallows up. It is said that a dozen back-to-nature middle class English bought up several farms in order to establish a "community" which soon collapsed in mutual recrimination. And a Scots whisky magnate bought up other farms and tried unsuccessfully to turn his tenants into crofters. More enduring are his grand plantations of Scots Pine.

Eastwards rises Stanky Hill, Black Mountain, and other bare hills, with abandoned clearances here and there, like New Invention. And then.
> At the end of a long sentence
> a full stop
> the English Border

Just across a little river another world—picturesque, prosperous and well-ordered. "Border View" smiles across at England.

> A sluggish river
> slowly unwinding
> the Border

A lugubrious nationalist tends his leeks; (he's a rarity among these Border folk). "Over there", he gestures with a dirty leek, "is somewhere else, where they're murdering the NHS and the poor must pay for their medicine". I cross the river boldly and—*Floreat Salopia!*—I am kindly received in the smiling and reasonable Englishry.

Later, back home across that river and haunted still, with renewed delight I wander those unwalked paths.

> Dawn and dusk
> summer and winter
> this land and I
> our stubborn selves

Broken Shotguns

> Walkie-talkie crackle
> the vixen and her cubs
> prick up their ears

At the edge of the forest we come upon a Land Rover. Slumped inside is an old man wearing a scruffy baseball cap. On the passenger seat a single barrelled shotgun, "broken" (hinged open) for safety. He switches off the walkie-talkie. In the absence of a fox a couple of hikers are a welcome enough surprise in these lonely mid-Wales hills.

The hunt area turns out to be several square miles of forestry and rough pasture, steep hills and narrow valleys. Foxes and hounds, hunters and us, we have it all to ourselves—with several hundred sheep, of course.

> A strident horn
> deep-throated hounds
> the sun strikes the covert

We come upon the hard core of the hunt, with a dozen frisky, floppy hounds. The local farmers, camouflaged in battledress fatigues. After a bit of chat about the lie of the land, we all set off—in opposite directions. Here no galloping horses, scarlet coats and blood-thirsty hounds. But plenty of new born lambs and hungry vixen. The hounds flush out the foxes and the farmers shoot them—with luck.

> Clomping along in wellies
> how homely
> the trill of his horn

"Alright?" He appears from nowhere. High on the moor we're lunching on our usual marital perches—here a pair of grassy tumps. A seasoned hunter, this one, clad head to foot in the muted colours of the hill. I covet his green moleskin shooting jacket. His Italian double-barrelled gun is a beauty. The lock's a finely engraved example of the gunsmith's art. "Brescia 1955". I squint down inside the broken-open barrels.

Two long smooth tubes
filled with sunlight
and innocence

Not fired once that day, by the smell of them. After the usual exchange about yesterday's rugby, we talk foxes. Their feral beauty. Those rare bewitching face-to-face encounters. The times he cannot squeeze the trigger. This hunter, how he loves his foxes!

Later we come upon a shooting stance.

Spent cartridges
a few fag ends
and a death foretold

⌐ ⌐ ⌐ ⌐ ⌐

Seven Pieces of Silver

Seven tall virgins
sacrificed
to make a winter's warmth

Backlit by sunsets and bending gracefully before the westerlies, our seven silver birches have grown pale and proud. Their tiny leaves dance and sparkle. Now, strung along the ridge, gripping a thin soil, they tower above the house. Their fate can no longer be postponed.

Through brittle sunlight
a shower of leaves
a day that lies in wait

Coward that I am, I delegate the felling to an old woodman who'll make a swift, clean job of it. He's not keen, but needs the money.

Without fuss, each one falls into its own long shadow. Only the seventh, ripped and torn, puts up a struggle

        Memorial stump
        I smother in moss
        its empty eye

The twigs and small branches, now a dismissive brash, are dumped into a hollow for the enjoyment of beetles. The firewood we cut, stack and wheelbarrow.

        Sawn up birch
        the innocence
        of pure white flesh

A "soft hardwood". Quietly it glows, silver and white, in its own corner of the wood shed.
        Birch and fir logs burn too fast
        blaze up bright but do not last
...says the old saw. Easy burning and easygoing, to the end.

Where once they stood, only the sky and the vacancy of loss. From every nook and cranny that last leaf-fall haunts our winter.

        On the worn headstone
        a dainty pink leaf
        held fast by wind and rain

Haiku

Through the mist
the Peak of the Three Lords
gathering darkness

A twilit line of thorn trees
ancient sentinels
against the dying light

From out of the dusk
her quiet *Nos da*
my distant neighbour

[*Nos da* (Welsh) "Good night"]

Winter twilight
the sheep flock silently
the mind falls still

Boulders in a mountain lake
clear to the bottom
without a thought

Moonlight on snow
 I follow the fox's tracks
into the dark wood

                              Grid reference
                              a patch of sunlight
                              on a distant hill

This smooth young spruce
her reflection
wrinkled by the moon

                              On which to sit
                              and ruminate my wrongs
                              a great black boulder

Across the moonlit mountain
a shared solitude
my distant neighbour's light

SAUNTERING

The Long Passage

> My shadow
> and my gammy leg
> out together for a walk

ATMOSPHERIC WALK is where it starts, with a shiny black bollard. Hidden in a row of semi-ds on a busy road. This backcrack slinks across our suburb past back gardens, back doors, back everything.

> PRIVATE
> fading on a back gate
> bound shut with ivy

Keeping company briefly with the railway line, it becomes THE METALS. Then it loses its identity for a while before picking up another. Further into town it becomes BOREEN this and that, in folksy Irish letters, embossed and green, De Valera vintage. Once it almost loses its nerve among the dreaded Silchesters—"Road", "Avenue", "Crescent", "Terrace", but a group of friendly wheelie bins helps it to get going again. Several road crossings later it finishes up among the children's swings of the People's Park and the salty tang of Dublin Bay.

> Sitting on shaven grass
> a seat with a view
> partnered by a litter bin

A walk for the Idle & Curious. On a back door, Tojo the Dwarf in elegant red letters, resprayed annually. Kept in thrall by a fair maiden?

Round a corner protected by spiky gothic ironwork: COMMIT NO NUISANCE. Caslon Old Face etched deep in granite, picked out with moss. Balloch harbour is only a skip and a jump away.

Sunday morning anglers
their solitude
enjoyed together

One is a James Joyce lookalike—reading, of course. "Any bites?"
"Enough to ruin a good read."

The strolling conviviality of the long, leisurely stretches melts the
misanthropic.

Pram-pushing dog walkers
icebreakers
of the Northwest Passage

Indeed, I suspect it is patrolled by a Secret Order of Panglossians,
dedicated to the elimination of melancholy. However, wasn't it Sam
Beckett who reminded us that ten minutes is long enough to spend
with anybody? A passing word and smile, our separate lives connect,
cross and are gone.

Broken free from its moorings
this absent mind
sailing the long passage

[Panglossians, after Dr Pangloss, in Voltaire's *Candide*, who believed that "All's for
the best in the best of worlds."]

~ ~ ~ ~ ~

Things To See and Do

Autumn again
the crazy paving
stained with rain

"Oh dear, how can we evade mortality, my love?"

"I know! Let's go to Belgium! Surely ten million people with five different governments and three hundred different beers will take us out of ourselves."

Flushed with enthusiasm, she is still a good looking woman. He rattles the ice in his Campari and soda, throws another log on the fire, and riffles the bible paper of the guide book:
> *The cathedral is a tad lop-sided... The crypt is stuffed with religious* bric à brac *of mild interest... The interior is a disappointment—an empty shell displaying a few old bells and statues... Tours of the Stadhuis are mildly enjoyable... A lugubrious C15th. cannon. The blackened remains of an antique torch snuffer."*

She claps her hands. "How perfectly ghastly! Do let's go, darling."

(Later, the same month)

Another coach-load of tourists has discharged outside the cathedral and joined the queue for Van Eyck's altarpiece.

"Adoration of the Mystic Lamb"—
cameras flash
in lieu of adoration

The torture chamber in the castle of the counts arouses less inhibited enthusiasm.

Municipal guillotine
a waxwork tourist
lies beheaded

A group of elderly Germans is more interested in the mechanism. The rack is a full-sized working replica, elegant in polished oak. *Vorsprung durch Technik*. For three Euros you can try your spouse out on it and get them to confess. A family photo opportunity. But a phlegmatic Englishman says it's nothing like as good as the Gestapo torture chamber near Mechlin.

A fitting end to the holiday, the Psychiatric Centre is reached by a high speed elasticated tramcar. At the Admissions desk a tiny grey paper disk is stuck on each tourist. Otherwise any attempt to distinguish between the madness in the Museum (from exorcism to Prozac) and that outside—in the courtyards, corridors and cafeteria of the hospital, (and beyond the tracks, for that matter)—has been abandoned. Everyone steals a shifty look at everyone else.

> He mutters past
> trying too hard
> to make sense

~ ~ ~ ~ ~ ~

Tram Fever

> A male heaven
> in a neat diagram
> the tram route map

Just off the Eurostar, in the morning of the world, I sit in an Antwerp pavement café. Here, at the centre of the map, the thickly bundled coloured strands. They lead out to the bold single ones which run off the edge of the map to unimaginable places.

At some of the stops, like "Kolonel Silvertop" and "Joe English" (between "Stenenbrug" and "Morckhova") I shall never alight, for fear of blighting my imagination. I remember Brussels, where you can get on at "Liverpool" and off at "Birmingham" only a few blocks away. But what about poor old "Simpson", dangerously close to the bilingual "Bombstraat / Rue de l'Obus"? Here in the Groenplaats, in the heart of Antwerp:

> At the terminus
> a metallic jostle
> of squeals and groans

All day long they curve through their maze of shining rails. The high numbers tend to be sleek, silent creatures with elasticated waists, serving the suburbs. Indeed, it was the tram network which made the suburbs possible. Like Antwerp's splendid *belle époque* Zurenborg, where an ecstatic Flemish poet has written in an underpass: *"Zurenborg brengt poëzie aan de tram"*. And, in turn, the tram brings its own poetry. So often, waiting in murky Brussels mornings, I've been cheered by the sight of a no. 92, a blaze of lights speeding out towards romantic "Fort Jaco". Some Belgian El Alamo, perhaps? I prefer not to know. Put me off at "St Job".

It is the older, shabbier trams which serve Antwerp's inner city, carrying within the exotic scents of immigration. *Ting-a-ling*. The poor man's chariots of fire! One night, alone, I recall being uncomfortably shadowed in the mean and dangerous streets beside the Scheldt,

> Over moonlit cobbles
> the redemptive clangor
> of a No. 9

Haiku

The tea room's well-bred tinkle
I clear my throat
adjust my tie

This place so well-preserved
in its hollow heart
not a soul

Holiday's end
we hungrily devour
the passing scene

The hour goes forward
the hour goes back
this long lifetime

Splattering gutters
and screaming gulls
Aberystwyth *mon amour*

on my paving slab
laid so long ago
this unnerving wobble

Table d'Hôte
on my shoulder
the touch of the waitress

~ ~ ~ ~ ~ ~

Fête champêtre
comme hors d'oeuvres
sycamore wings

Fête champêtre
comme viande
a bull's bellow

Fête champêtre
comme dégustation
murmur of the stream

LOVE AND LUST

An End to It

> The street lights end
> to the throb of the wipers
> their dark road unwinds

His car or hers, and the snug of some out-of-the-way pub. As to the rear seats, the years of yoga helped. Two guilty outlaws concealed by darkness and dim light, or else those remote weekends. In the end, only the cats' eyes.

Some modest consolations will remain. She'd never enjoyed Bruckner's symphonies before they met. Now she did. Also some new poets he ushered into her pantheon. But the letters she would burn.

Slowing down now; his Triumph Herald caught in her headlights, standing as usual beneath the birches at the cross roads. A dry kiss. He gets out carefully; closes the door gently. Flashes his headlights twice—their old sign. "The coast is clear". Accelerates away with a certain *panache*. Back to a cold wife and an honourable life. "FIN" —his art-house film is over; the lights go up.

> Above a mossy boulder
> the frenzied dance
> of two grey moths

~ ~ ~ ~ ~

A Tale of Master John Goodfellow and the Velveteen Mousetrap

> Tall ghosts
> of winter larches
> a gently swaying sadness

Once upon a time, when I was old, I received this carnal knowledge of a tale of faerie music. How the majestic melancholy of my

Bruckner adagios would fade away in her light-hearted presence!

"Ride a cock horse to Banbury Cross"

—she would croon as she rose and fell, jig-a-jig jig, the joy in her breasts.

"See this fine lady on an 'ole hoss.
With rings on her fingers and bells on her toes
She shall have music wherever she goes."

All the while she would laugh, and afterwards carry on with her knitting. A purple muffler for a young lover. But she was always happy enough to be taken for a ride, so long as my muse could conjure up a bawdy haiku for her. For these she had a curious talent to set to song.

Ah! Ancient Monument
how shrunk and pale
this frozen molehill

[Master John Goodfellow—In Urquhart's *Rabelais* (1653) II,21: "Master John Goodfellow, that askes for lodging", that is, the natural member.]

[This haibun was first performed live on 18 March 2011 at the Dylan Thomas Centre, Swansea. The narrator was accompanied by Maggie Nichol (singer) and Peter Stacey (clarinet and saxophone).]

~ ~ ~ ~ ~ ~

A Season Out of Mind

"Fin-de-siècle gent wltm lady to share interest in asceticism and ecclesiology"
New Statesman & Nation, October 196—

Castaway on a western shore, in a wind-blown grove of academe. A matrimonial refugee, with a change of underwear and an unfinished thesis: *"The viability of public library services in towns of below 30,000 population."* Each week he received a letter from his abandoned wife—her small, round hand on Blue Vellum. And often another, from his abandoned mistress—a demented scrawl on ruled feint.

> Torn-open letters
> two seagulls worry
> a long-dead dogfish

Each weekend he would flee the thesis and the lecturing on the Dewey Decimal Classification. Solace in the arms of spirited women, keen to "share my interest in literature and walking". But now a very different small ad to bait the hook. Weary and guilty at whom he was, and the tedium of the priapic life, he yearned to be Somebody Else , at least at the weekends.

Day dreaming in my window, Rodin's *Thinker*

The only reply came from sixty miles away, over the border in England. An arts-and-crafts lady in an arts-and-crafts villa. She had vacancies for characters in her vast and never ending *fin-de-siècle* novel. Would he care to apply? His big chance to become Somebody Else?

Top marks, too, for ecclesiology. She knew a leper squint when she saw one. And gave a cry of delight when they discovered a Caroe chapel in some remote rural church.

Asceticism?
More than a friend
less than a lover
we size each other up

Her bedroom door was always left just a fraction open. For their peculiar purpose the heart-strings needed to be not too loose and not too tight.

Every weekend that winter they played characters from the literature and culture of England and France in the late 19th and early 20th centuries. By agreement in advance they ad-libbed the typical sensibilities and concerns of the age. It took quite a lot of reading up and rehearsal to become as much Somebody Else as they could— especially if it was his turn to concoct a *belle époque* dinner and serve *apéritifs* in the topiary garden.

A searching breeze
shifty clouds
swirling round our unfamiliar selves

Tall and eloquent, she had something in her wardrobe for every occasion, and her art nouveau gowns filled him with pre-Raphaelite fervour. He recalled a particularly demanding weekend when they had agreed to be French romantics.

Fleurs du mal
her arch gestures
his rolling eyes

The Alfred Lord Tennyson weekend was a lot easier. He fondly recalled the Lady of Shallott's welcome to his rickety VW Beetle:

"A bowshot from her bower eaves
He rode between the barley sheaves"

It was always difficult wrenching himself back into his work-a-day persona on those freezing dawn Mondays. In George Sand's kitchen, Chopin retrieving the warmed up spark plugs from the oven.

Of course, it couldn't last. On that last departure they briefly lied about who they were in ordinary life.

> Our silence at breakfast
> her long slow wink

~ ~ ~ ~ ~ ~

Leonora

> On the rack of an old man's cough
> at dawn I confess
> these sweet bitter dreams

Once upon a time, in a south Wales valley, there lived a woman called Leonora. How can I forget the flamenco swirl of her brightly coloured skirts? So come with me, *bach,* to the little coffee house she inherited from her Italian father. This is a place of slate-roofed terraces, dominated by pit heads and slag-heaps. In the coffee-house is a giant Gaggia coffee machine, of polished silver, topped with an eagle spreading its wings. It towers above the sawdust floor and the sepia photos of Turin.

It is a time of high unemployment and deep poverty. It turns out that Leonora is a *Garibalidina* and that her great-grandfather was a Red Shirt, one of Garibaldi's famous Thousand. Already the lads of the South Wales Miners' Federation have added *"The Red Flag"* to the pub's traditional repertoire of *"Sospan Fach"* and *"Cwm Rhondda"*. And now the Italian version has spread from coffee house to pub.
> *Avanti o popolo alla riscossa*
> *Bandiera rossa la trionferà*
Gathered in the coffee house the Party members and fellow politicals

read the papers and discuss the defence of the Spanish Republic against Franco's fascists. Soon we're bidding farewell to the young men leaving to join the International Brigade.

> Clenched fists raised
> the shriek of the engine
> the thrust of its pistons

And soon the whispering begins. About the love—and courage—which she gives them. And not only them but older men too. But, *chware teg*, in the hard times has not almost everyone received some help and kindness from Leonora?

However, it is the intimate passion of body and mind which can work the deepest magic. She seems to have imprinted a habit of kindness even on unlikely hearts.

> Her rumpled sheets
> her flowering plants
> her sunlight on slate roofs

Many of our best have never returned. Unmarked graves on the banks of the Ebro. One wet Monday evening, lingering alone over my *cappuccino*, I hear her behind the Gaggia, winding up that gramophone of hers. Between Verdi's swooping melodies her quiet weeping.

> Wound up with vigour
> *The Force of Destiny*
> and then the voices fade.

[The Welsh mining valleys were at one time home to a flourishing Italian immigrant community, famed for their ice cream parlours and coffee houses.]

[Leonora—the name of the heroine of Verdi's tragic opera *Il Trovatore*]

[*Bach* (Welsh) "Little", used as a term of familiarity and endearment.]

[*Chware teg* (Welsh) "Fair play".]

The Ascent

No passing places
squeezed between rough walls
they motor on

Abandoning the Little Red Racer, there lies a track which fades into
a path which fades into nothing.

The long walk in
each their own distinctive boot print
left in the mud

Round his neck the bright red compass cord. And this frozen crescent
lake is the bleak place where they are supposed to be. Suddenly,
through a bitter wind, their looming mountain, made larger through
the drifting mist—Pen Olau: the Peak of Light.

Thirty years ago they climbed and courted here, making short work
of both. Now, crouched behind a boulder, unspoken fear is soon
forgotten in each fivefold sandwich—pickle, Caerphilly cheese,
lettuce, tomato and mayonnaise. He traces a gloved finger across the
orange contour lines which chart their wilderness.

Losing their way
his biro'd arrows
smudged by rain

"Okay! Let's go!" She picks her way surefooted up through a chaos of
boulders, followed by the click-clicking of his trekking poles.
Suddenly the mist lifts, revealing an awesome bastion of Cambrian
slate. Set against it is their lifetime knack of finding a way up through
the impossible.

Arthritic joints
up though jointed slabs
"Pussycat—will it go?"

They drag themselves up onto a slate dance floor and waltz a few steps in their mountain boots, sheer drops on every side. Then more bone against hard rock, ruby ringed fingers jammed into the cracks. Together still, each finds their own best way.

> Above a sea of mist
> our sunlit summit

~ ~ ~ ~ ~

The Path

> Our path fades out
> as time fades out
> he passes her the compass

Twisting the map, he peers at the faint pecked line of an ancient and elusive path. "North by north-west, pussy cat!" She squints at the flickering needle... Points a steady arm. "North by north-west, pug dog!"

Whooping downhill in a shower of pebbles and dead leaves, splashing across the stream, and up into the trees, before they're out of breath. And, behold! the old path awaits them.

~ ~ ~ ~ ~

Haiku

Rack and pinion
a perfect fit
their life together

Laughing away together
how little
we dare to say

In the sacred grove
she hears the angels
and his cell phone comes to life

After the film
the silence
of the long drive home

Where once her pictures hung
only vacant stares

A photo she left—
solitude
lurches back to loneliness

Two tree stumps
close enough for a couple
to keep their distance

Climbing the deer fence
then bog myrtle miles
to meet you at the ruin

The long hike
resting in a Bronze Age circle
they discuss their love life

A breakfast
of matrimonial banter
how the bacon sizzles!

Ancient love
our mulled wine
thinned with apple juice

Husband and wife
bringing home the firewood
singing in the setting sun

"Loving Memory"
on a keeling headstone
blotched with white lichen

THINGS AREN'T WHAT THEY SEEM

Insentient Beings

Ah, these early breakfasts, alone with my three perverse companions. "Hi, guys! Wakey, wakey!"

The toaster is a curmudgeonly old fellow, unpredictable in his behaviour. Except that he detests brown bread. Probably a racist.

> Shot high in the air
> with a fearsome finality
> two blackened faces

More intriguing is my dove grey electric kettle. Calls herself "Russell Hobbs" and is probably a transvestite. Now she's growing old and scaled up she, too, has developed a will of her own. It had always been easy to turn her on, but now she takes a long time to warm up. And then she turns off when just getting to the boil. I have to sit at the table, wondering what she's feeling, and longing for my tea.

> Mute and resentful
> one red eye shut
> her ON/OFF life

And in the background there's that plop! plop! plop! The *basso continuo* of the cold tap.

> No two quite the same
> his eccentric dripping
> warms my heart

Of course, I could re-washer the tap, descale the kettle, and throw out the toaster. But how could I bear such an existential deficit so early in the day?

Satisfaction Guaranteed

> Dead toaster
> the autopsy frustrated
> by knurled nuts

To bring it back to life we turn to the INSTRUCTIONS folder, sandwiched between a French beard trimmer manual and all you need to know about the Funkwecker Radio-Controlled Alarm Clock. Alas, no dramatic Exploded Parts Diagram—to every humble grub screw its unique number. We trawl the aseptic text for signs of humanity. There are some mildly lyrical—even compassionate—moments, as in the advice to *"remove any loose raisins from the surface of the bread... this will help them from falling into the toaster"*. Hapless crumpets are more summarily dealt with—*"Slice each crumpet into equal halves."*

Generally the mood is one of anxiety—even mild neurosis. *"Bread may burn! This toaster must be watched!"* And there are some dark but vaguely suggestive warnings: *"Do not use this appliance for other than its intended use."*

Under "TOASTING NOTES" the "owner/operator" is taken more seriously in hand, beginning with the fundamental proposition that *"Toasting is a combination of cooking and drying the bread"*. The writing becomes so fretfully didactic as to suggest it is the work of one of Adorno's "Authoritarian Personality Types", possibly a fascist and spouse-beater. And the following is decidedly esoteric:

"Applicable for custom-made-face on toast ONLY. Generally speaking, the higher browning controls setting, the higher the quality of custom-made-face toast. Experience it yourself & enjoy the toast!"

Note the sudden generosity of spirit at the end. It moves Noragh to draw a *"custom-made-face"* on the inert toaster, as a kind of wish-fulfilment magic. Meanwhile, from the fault-finding section I sketch out a decision-tree, to which she adds a few crows.

We try to give the writer a more sympathetic ear. And then, in an obscure corner of the text, he or she observes off-handedly that *"the handle may not latch if the browning control is set to minimum."* Yes indeed!

Surely one area of life where *"Satisfaction is Unreservedly Guaranteed".*

> *Clack!*
> Two perfect slices
> shoot out into this troubled world

~ ~ ~ ~ ~ ~

Alter Ego

> Those erratic movements
> and that fixed smile
> how like a puppet!

Thrust your hand, glove-like, into this vividly coloured scrap of cloth and *papier-mâché*. Thumb into the head, fingers into the arms. Ungainly at first, another life stirs. Just like us, it acts out a story. Perhaps a story we cannot live ourselves, except through our fingers. A story in the gestures and the face. With a speechless papier-mâché smile he stills each movement, giving time for us to guess his thoughts.

Larger than life, those fixed expressions. The wide-eyed simpleton. The down-in-the-mouth melancholic. The self-important frown. The big argumentative mouth. The scheming eyes like slits.

Madam has made a puppet, Towzer, which she thinks embodies me. And I have shaped and painted her, with even more flamboyant clothes and hair-do. When we feel a matrimonial argument creeping up on us, we put on the glove puppets and leave it to these two to get on with the game. With gestures that are strangely familiar.

Dancing on invisible strings
brightly clad puppets
we enact our lives

~ ~ ~ ~ ~ ~

Deconstruction

I snap up the blinds
another day
takes me in for questioning

In the mirror, a suspicious character. Off to the art gallery, where I know I can become a reassured somebody once more, so long as I stick to the representational stuff. Wandering through those Dutch domestic interiors or strolling through the lush pastures of Albert Cuyps's placid cows I feel at home again.

Later, refreshed and emboldened, I head for the exit. Only to be waylaid by Postmodernism. Sitting on a bench in one of its empty rooms I watch a video—a random succession of stills with voice-over, deconstructing my precarious reality.

A wilderness so featureless
that nowhere exists
except on the map

The nearest thing to a map is the exhibition catalogue:

Hello. It's as hard to say anything that is as good as saying nothing. So I made some things...Let's call them videos....Little happens. Little that I could describe, anyway. If I did describe them it would probably be irrelevant to anything you want to know...I don't know where they are going. Things rub together. It's risky. It necessitates making and avoiding choices. They proceed from half-digested notions propped up with contradictory information.

The spinning compass
and my spinning head
nothing where it ought to be

Staggering out into the sunshine I recall reading somewhere of a similar experience of David Hume, the great philosopher of the Scottish enlightenment. Apparently his solitary cogitations so undermined his belief in his own existence that he had to flee into the next room to take refuge with his friends playing a game of billiards.

Each in our own way
we grip the empty clothes line
we well-worn pegs

Across the street the pool table in the Ship Inn does me a like service of reconstruction.

Joshing with friends
eye on the ball
I chalk my cue

[With grateful acknowledgement the catalogue extract above is taken from an exhibition by Heather Phillipson at the Aberystwyth Arts Centre, April-May 2011. A leaflet explains that *she combines influences from cinema, literature and the visual arts with the everyday mundane objects close to hand, undermining systems of meaning and prescribed associations.*]

⌐ ⌐ ⌐ ⌐ ⌐

Colophon

This slim volume
of lyrical verse
my neighbour's wife

There she lies, on my desk, appropriated and reified in Perfect Binding, the kind that comes apart all too easily—but coveted nonetheless. With infinite grace in brittle sunshine she hangs out the family washing. Up there with Donne she'd never guess herself possessed by a marbled and slightly foxed old neighbour, lusty once, now bound in buckram and reading out his final years.

the warm sun
brightens an old carpet
as it passes

Haiku

Drinking water
from her wine glass
the red azalea

With one deft blow
I top my boiled egg
its lovely smile

Full English breakfast
staring at the black pudding
staring back at me

So many black down-pipes
thrusting skywards
into the blue

From its flat pack
a skinny sawing horse
bolted, braced and hungry

Stained on glass
and breathing floor polish
Victorian saints

Shaky bridge
this calm day I cross the water
on its shadow

Swags of fruit and flowers
their cast iron symmetry
makes my fragile day

His face
scarred by a scudding cloud
this old man in the moon

Lost in a wind
this smooth stone
its bitter grains of sand

The lie of the land
tracing across bogs
her manicured finger

                    Frozen meadow
                a soft black molehill
                    lifts the heart

A LIFE

An Afternoon at the Biographicum

> On the stony path
> where my shadow points
> I follow

Up a previously unknown way through the woods. And in a clearing a rusty storage container bearing the faded letters LUX TRANSIT LOGISTICS. Idly and at random I flip the metal digits of its combination lock and, rather to my alarm, the door slides open. A reassuring backward glance over the great estuary of the Dyfi, spread out below the forest.

> The sea gone out
> across the grain of the fluted sands
> cloud shadows drift

Inside is what looks like an airline seat in a small chamber resembling a planetarium. Musak of the tinkling spheres. A younger self stares out of a screen. *"Is this you? (select and click) Welcome to the Skull Cinema!"* A row of role folders pops up on the screen—teacher, spouse, politico, lover, ascetic and so on.

I click on "Son" and a memorable childhood episode begins to play through, like a video, or, rather, in this case, an old film. I see it all through my child's eyes, and can hear that voice only too well (bullying my sister, as it happens), except it sounds different before seventy years of hard wear. After such a long time I'm a stranger to myself. There's our chocolate-coloured bakelite wireless. And here's my anxious mother, with her emotional hunger, wearing that fur boa with the fox's pointy face. In grainy black and white I relive a life with the irrepressible dead.

Some more recent episodes in other roles have a shattering immediacy; things are not as I now recall (though I was apparently better at billiards). "No, don't do it!" I mutter (like, turn down that job offer, or chat up that woman). But I do. Or, rather, he does. And often, well-deservedly, someone else does, too. Some of the episodes sign off with my/his favourite music of that time. Operatic Verdi can make even folly sound like fun. *La Forza del Destino.*

Somewhere a heavy coin clunks into a metal box, and EXIT lights up. A moment of panic. But the lights do come on. An affable functionary, with *Biographicum* on his jacket, offers me a complimentary drink at the little bar. "Enjoy the show, sir?" I hasten out past the "Personalised Souvenirs" and into brittle winter sunshine.

> Estuary flowing with light
> flood tide
> fingering new channels

I glance around for fear of alter-egos, doppelgangers or the like waiting to waylay me, and make sure my shadow is coming too. Then off for tea and buttered welsh cakes at the Penhelig Arms.

> Again that broken stony path
> but not a single pebble
> out of place

～ ～ ～ ～ ～

Out on the Knocker

> We the faithful
> gathered at the cross
> clutching our clipboards

Armed with canvass cards and "literature" we fan out across a bleak and unsuspecting housing estate. To the clack-clack of letter boxes we shove home the fixed smiles of the candidate, his wife and his kids.

First a tiny manicured garden. Across the taut chain on her door

"Not today thanks—not interested".

Next door I hear a child scrambling upstairs at my approach. "Mam! MAM! There's a MAN at the door!" Mam points to the ceiling in the children's bedroom.

> Lank hair
> anxiety in her eyes
> the damp stain spreads

Lamely I tell her I'll get onto the housing association.

Further along a house abandoned, its windows broken.

> "Gone Away"
> in the long grass
> a beat-up rocking horse

"Fuckin' nationalist!" she screams at my hunched shoulders, retreating down her path. Unsurprisingly her neighbour keeps a red dragon in his garden. The thin earnest man with wire rimmed glasses won't let me go: "Just think, man—if us and the Scots got independence we could share an aircraft carrier between us!"

A door opens. "You can't trust any of 'em—they're all tarred with the same brush!" The door closes.

> Over the years
> his grudge becomes his face
> his small change turns to rancour

Outside in the road a man whistles as he lovingly polishes his Robin Reliant. A shared passion here. Excitedly we chat about the dear dead days of Isettas, Heinkels and other classic three-wheeled cars. Then, as an afterthought, "Pob hwyl, bach! We're solid here, except for mam, who always votes for the other lot."

Back at the café, over mugs of industrial-strength tea we enjoy door-step stories and political banter. *"Plato thought democracy a bad idea. Discuss."*

> "For" "Against" "Don't know"
> there's a twinkle in her eye
> all that falls between

["Red dragon" - the Welsh national flag]
[*"Pob hwyl, bach!"* – "Right on, lad!"]

~ ~ ~ ~ ~ ~

Gift of the Gab

> Public lecture
> the metallic screech
> of stacking chairs

The yellow and green distemper of the Lloyd George Memorial Hall. A wet evening, with a few solitaries huddled at the back, their collars up. Three or four youths standing and whispering by the door, ready to leave. A young woman from *The Cambrian News*, clutching a notebook, sneaks in. Like everyone else she avoids my smile. And nearest the front, legs crossed, arms crossed, and staring straight ahead, is trouble. He refuses to be drawn. It's already a quarter past when a promising pair from the Women's Institute come bustling in.

The tweedy, beaming chairman thanks me for "filling the gap". "Now I must leave you all in Mr Jones's safe hands". I come down from the platform and stand in the empty front row, smile on face and hands in pockets. A clothes-peg in the left one and what appears to be an aged Murray Mint in the other. Silence. Then more silence.

In the old tea urn
an empty echo
Plop!

And then I hear a voice. Mine. The hall becomes a theatre. A woman
near the front, with cropped white hair, gives an encouraging smile.
A nod here, a chuckle there; slowly the mood spreads. Together my
audience and I take off.

Set on the gas stove
the battered kettle
begins to sing

"I'm glad you asked that. Yes, it's an interesting one" He uncrosses
arms and legs and leans forward. Others are drawn in. At the end
several come up for a chat. The white haired lady buys some of "the
literature" and asks me to sign.

Hands are shaken, my briefcase clicks shut, and I'm out alone.
Which is how it is.

Swaying
on an empty clothes-line
a sky of stars

~ ~ ~ ~ ~

La Vie en Rose

Dogwood's delight
even in winter
its twigs aflame

Through his hotel window the rococo town hall is already floodlit and proclaiming, in letters of gold, *"Liberté, Egalité, Fraternité"*

The panama hat, with the black band, worn not so rakishly nowadays. But he's still a dab hand at tipping it to a lady. Then there's the cane and carnation of the true *flâneur*. Finally, a light touch of eau de cologne. He squares his shoulders and strides forth, to tread once more that delicate thin line.

In the big gilded mirror of the restaurant he observes, with smiling eyes, that noisy bustle. The dinner—*poulet bonne femme*, accompanied by a Pouilly-Fumé—is just right. Then his favourite *entremets*—an omelette sprinkled with rum. Ripe now for a little delicate flirting with the waitress. True, his French is rather Third Republic vintage, but he gets by well enough, with *"une vieille habitude, mam'selle"*, and a slight shrug of the shoulders.

Thence to *"Le Bouffon Sage"*, on the cobbled Place Ducale.

Napoleon brandy
between each sip
heaven and earth are one

And still further so with a well-presented *petit noir* and the deep fragrance of a Bolivar Havana.

Alertness mellowed, mind at rest, he produces a well thumbed translation of the *Hsin-hsin-ming*—On Trust in the Heart:
'When the mind is undisturbed, nothing offers offence... When you are not antagonistic to the world of the senses it is the same as complete enlightenment'.

73

Eyebrows raised, he finds himself peering over his reading glasses at the evening parade of chic elegance.

The midnight chimes of Notre Dame d'Espérance break the spell. Another brandy? Mere self-indulgence, he mutters to himself, leaving his tip.

> Deep in winter grasses
> an ancient stone
> dreams its long life

[*Flâneur*: a stroller.]
[Pouilly Fumé: a fine white wine of the Loire region.]
[*Le Bouffon Sage*: "The Wise Jester".]
[*Petit noir:* espresso coffee.]

~ ~ ~ ~ ~

Sibelius and I

Fourth Symphony

> Depressing "START"
> his music
> my sadness

Jagged brass chords, fragmentary winds, and piercing cries from the violins fill my inner landscape. On another bad day, a hundred years ago, in Karelia, he strains his ears to catch the polyphony of the wild falls of Imatra. *"The sighing of the winds and the roar of the storms"*. The furies subside and the *adagio* begins.

> Slowly a sombre horn
> swells to some sunlit world
> of strings and brass

Played at his funeral. To be played at mine.

An audience hissed; an orchestra refused to play. This confirmed the life-long self-doubt that plagued him. "I am spoilt, superior and weak-willed," he lamented. Behind his whisky grin and big cigar, his shrinking ego.

Pohjola's Daughter

On days when I feel I could tie an egg into invisible knots, I join his biggest and most boisterous orchestra in the pursuit of the daughter of Pohjola the magician. Careering along after Pohjola's daughter how simple life is!

Late at night the pot-boilers he composed to clear his debts. I conduct a huge orchestra playing Finlandia. Or enjoy the schmaltzy kitsch of the *Valse Triste*:

> Sweeping around
> the empty ballroom
> of my cramped study

Fifth Symphony

> *Ahng—ha! Ahng-ha!*
> trumpet the whooper swans—
> and the year turns

Lifting off from their grazings here beside our Dyfi estuary, the strong, steady beat of their wings. So it was with Sibelius, swept along by the flight of sixteen swans above his house at Ainola, one day in April, 1915.

One of my greatest experiences! Lord God, that beauty! Their call the same woodwind type as cranes, but without tremolo. The swan-call closer to the trumpet, although there is something of a saxophone sound... Nature mysticism and life's Angst! The Fifth Symphony's finale-theme: Legato in the trumpets!!

Seventh Symphony

> Life as symphony
> strings and trombones
> weave its coloured threads

Nothing had ever been heard before like this. Night after night the writing—and the drinking. In the morning his long-suffering wife Aino would remove the empties from beside the slumped figure.

Music stripped to its bare essentials. A single river of sound, flowing through thematic twists and turns to the climax of a life complete.

Tapiola

Howling through my backwoods, "ancient, mysterious, and brooding dreams"—Tapio, the forest god. Just one short theme throughout, mounting to an explosion for the whole orchestra. All chords in the minor key—except the last.

The rest is thirty years of silence. Lit by the fire of a "grand burning party" of all his scores in progress. The Eighth was never seen by anyone but him.

> *Diminuendo*
> outside my window
> the brook murmurs on

An Appointment with Yama

> Vanishing in the smoke
> of burning leaves
> a weathered Buddha

At the Enno-ji temple in Kamakura the Lord of Death is in session with his ten officials at their desks. Hardwood carvings, life-sized. Not so much a judge and jury. More a data-processing unit of functionaries, assessing my life story and making the necessary karmic calculations for a favourable or unfavourable rebirth. For the terminally ill a waiting room is provided for creative writing, to pass the time.

> EXIT sign
> the intensity of waiting
> at a revolving door

The past four years, on the first of each month, I have been presenting myself to one of the officials. He gives me that "Not you again!" look and, out of the side of his mouth, a decimal number. If the number—stable until now—has commenced to rise, the spell has broken and it's time to pack my bags.

And so, on the last days of each month (like these) my sky begins to darken. Then—so far—it lightens again. And for about three weeks I can rejoin the throng who feel they are immortal.

> Crazy fence
> every barb
> rich in rust

~ ~ ~ ~ ~

The Brass Name Plate

> Winding through reeds
> to the crumbling dyke
> and the endless sea beyond

Mortality traced out in small blue squares—those four fat years of immortal flat-lining. But this clinical statistic has suddenly taken an alarmingly steep upward curve towards the inscription at the top of the sheet: **Sic Transit**. Now I must play my last card against my deadly adversary Adenocarcinoma (otherwise known as Big C).

> At the window
> how frantically it beats
> against its own reflection

The card is Dr Pfeifer's Magick Protocol. This means it's Harley Street at £300 a throw (just for starters).

So many highly polished brass name plates on every stately door. In the empty waiting room a chandelier hangs above an onyx table. No dog-eared back numbers of *The National Geographic* here, let alone *Hello!* magazine. Instead, bound volumes of surgical journals line the walls. I dip into one and, at the first diagram, hastily replace it.

Brisk and bangled, the receptionist ushers me in with a refined gesture.

> Between Him
> and me
> three feet of polished walnut

He drones the litany of pills and potions which constitute the Protocol, and with which I am to stock my medicine cabinet. Zeolite, to rid me of my heavy metals, "taken from volcanic rock and tribo-mechanically activated". *Resveratrol*, "red wine extract (with grape skins)" and costing more than a good Beaujolais. Then there are more homely pills, like Natto, made from *"fermented soya beans"*, with a reassuring Pomegranate Complex at the bottom of the list. At least nothing here to rack me with the side-effects promised by conventional treatments.

Mesmerised, I gaze out of the window. Behind rows of chimney stacks mares' tails drift in a pale blue sky.

"Mr Jones! Do you have any questions?"

Only the unanswerable ones.

> Off-shore wind
> the heaving shingle
> tumbling my thoughts

[*Harley Street* – In London, a by-word for the high end of medical treatments.]

~ ~ ~ ~ ~

Haiku

"Things to do today"
I tick off
my life

Discounted life
a wallet stuffed
with loyalty cards

In the convex mirror
my convex room
my concave life

All day long
the mist drifts round
the edges of my solitude

In grey light
beneath landscapes on the wall
empty clothes

Beneath a hazy moon
I rattle concepts
round my silly skull

In a crowd
the conspiratorial smile
of another old man

Twentieth Century Dictionary
wearing out
our lives together

Old age—
now a stranger
smiling in my mirror

Navigating
the shipwrecks of my life
and at the end
the sprung alarm,

At the end of The Manual
a sigh of relief
This page is intentionally blank

THE GRAVE AND CONSTANT

*"When man in his agony is dumb we have God's
gift to utter what we suffer".*
            Goethe

Honour and Glory

Hee-haw! hee-haw!
saluting the imperial standard
a brazen ass

The Journal of a Siege: 1st May 17--

Written in a dank, iron casemate. Only on a peaceful summer do
these forts, so artfully conceived by Monsieur de Vauban, look their
most elegant. All was prepared before the investment, now in its
second month, had begun.

Ravelins and counterscarps
clad all in sweet green grass
mown ready for the dead

They have yet to bring up their siege guns; their cannon balls disturb
us little.

Dawn chorus
abruptly halted
by a cannonade

The commandant assures me that as soon as matters become
seriously heroic he will feel free to negotiate an honourable surrender.
And so I pen a letter to my wife regarding the spring sowing on my
estate. And another to my mistress offering a little *badinage* in well-
turned couplets. The latter end in a scrawl. as the earth shakes
beneath me. A mine! A mine! The insistent bugle. The clatter of
ammunition boots. Buckling on my sword I hasten to my post.

Here they come, plodding up the *glacis*. A turkey shoot, just as
Monsieur de Vauban had planned.

Across the future dead
he lays his rule
his fields of fire

After the dense black smoke has cleared we see the execution our flintlocks have wrought amongst them. The living are struggling back up the counterscarp. They leave behind the grotesque dead and the screaming wounded. Poor fellows! We either work them to death at home like horses or else we enlist them to be shot at the behest of other well-mannered gentlemen.

> Clockwork soldiers
> lost in their own smoke
> they blaze at one another

I am ordered to arrange a parlay for the recovery of the wounded, the burial of the dead and the exchange of prisoners. With shivers down my spine, I step out with a little drummer boy and a tall serjeant bearing a white flag. Their officers are grand fellows and invite me to their mess. An excellent claret. Toasts to their king and our empress.

> *Eau-de-Cologne* and powdered wigs
> exchanging snuff
> and prisoners

Protected by the Articles of War I am duly returned to our lines. A calm, clear night. Beyond the encirclement a farm dog is howling.

> Beneath a low slung moon
> besiegers and besieged
> dream each others' dreams

[*Note:* This fragment was found on the body of an unknown officer after the storming of Fort S--- ended a prolonged and destructive siege.]

Love and Silence

One by one the retreatants arrive. Sip tea. Hang about. Guarded. Expectant. I gather them in a circle of black cushions. They eye one another. And they eye me, and my premature smile. The first talk opens with a silence, not too long not too short. To every phrase its own space. Hopefully I scan the faces for signs of making sense. It takes time to draw them in, one by one, for our journey to begin.

> Worn clipboard
> the spring still grips
> my scribbled thoughts

Before dawn, the *Crack! Crack!* of the wake-up clappers. Muffled figures shuffle into the yard, with its hissing lamps and pools of rainwater. Following my creaky gestures, our physical jerks begin. And then some watchwords for the day.

> Wind-blown—
> an empty can
> rattles over cobbles

Back inside I glance along the lines of meditators. An awesome stillness hangs in the air. To each skull cinema its own films: old news reels, future trailers, or maybe the big picture itself. Or even a blank screen. Or perhaps the projectionist has already gone home? Through lidded eyes, downward gaze at forty-five degrees. Ah! I see him steal a restless glance. And she gets the message.

> Retreat romance
> ripened
> by the rule of silence

Interviews, one by one. Together we watch the sky turn pale above the great field. Through a fretted line of trees a tiny light. She fingers the stitching of her leather chair. And starts to tell me…

By the second evening the retreat has taken on a life of its own, and carries us along with it. Inside, as well as outside, the weather is what it needs to be.

> Into our shared silence
> a howling wind
> a beating rain

I have them gather in groups of four around a "speaking stone." To share with one another each their unwinnable lawsuit against reality. And perhaps to empty their hearts.

> Cupping the hand-warmed stone
> feeling its jagged edges
> he lets it speak

Five days of gathered silence. Enough to thaw the love between strangers.

The group photo includes the Goddess of Compassion in black teak. From her shrine she is looking over someone's shoulder, a hand raised in blessing.

~ ~ ~ ~ ~ ~

The Fall

> Through the haze the sun
> a silver shilling
> fallen on the shore

Five Mile Beach in a sepia spring. Vast and still and empty, an outstretched world of sand and sea and dunes. Lost in wonder, hand in hand we walk the margin of our lives.

This lazy sea
drawn by an unseen moon
across the ribs of sand

A far off couple—time enough to weave them in the spell. Young lovers in this morning of the world? But here they come, looking through us ancient ghosts, unseeing they pass by.

He shouting in his cellphone
she frowning in the void

Let sea, sand and sky reclaim us, splashing through the shallows of our final years.

~ ~ ~ ~ ~

The Lost and the Found

Within earshot of the Atlantic breakers, this Hebridean graveyard. The headstones are as varied and scattered as the croft houses of the living. But in the far corner there stands a uniform granite line. A few bear names, nationalities, dates:

Birger Oest-Larsen
Danish Merchant Navy
Found
6 January 1942

As I walk west into the wind the inscriptions become simpler:

A SAILOR
of the 1939-1945 War
Royal Navy
Found
21 August 1940

Finally, only this:

FOUND
A SAILOR
November 1943

Known Only to God

Torn by the rocks then cast on the shore. *Lost At Sea* for those who knew him. Then found, but known only to God.

Blast from the sea
driving salt rain
through dry-stone walls

~ ~ ~ ~ ~ ~

The Dying

Each morning
if the sun shows up
together we climb the hill

For now the turning world is squeezing the sunshine out of the deep valley of the Rheidol. So each morning I have to climb higher and higher behind the house to reach my bright, warm-hearted companion. There I find her just peeping through the saw-edged line of spruce which fringes the skyline on the other side of the valley.

Twilight in *Coed Simdhe Llwyd*—Grey Chimney Wood—now haunted by the yellow fronds of dying bracken, standing spectral in the stillness of the evening. The bracken, the silent oaks, and this old man, all bewitched together.

Cutting through my reverie
the sharp splatter of rain
on dead leaves

Stone Age

Prehistoric pillar
on its face
a dance of mayflies

I plant my eighty-one year old shadow in the circle surrounding the Menhir, the great standing stone. My folding chair squeaks uneasily. For each of the stones in the circle stands for five years of my life.

Just a few, wind washed and worn, preserve their innocence. Others are jagged, fickle and best forgotten. Then there are the veined white quartz stones, the good luck stones, best remembered. And what about those still displaying their brightly coloured lichens? And the austere granite one that sits bolt upright? I try to get a group discussion going among them, but they only respond with their lifetimes of stony stares.

Quiet stones
not one of them
troubled

The rotating shadow of the Menhir has fallen on each in turn, slowly devouring those 81 x 365 sunrises. For he, the Ancient of Days, has witnessed 7 x 52 x 3,000 sunsets—more or less.

I rise from my seat
the silence that fills the circle
none of it mine

[*Menhirs*—tall stones dating from the Bronze Age.]

Bog Cotton

Why did he return
to that empty island?
bog-cotton in the wind
Kenneth White

A warning buoy
rolling heavy in the sound
the tolling of its bell

"Good—I see you've left your baggage behind!" exclaims the sullen ferryman, "for you would have no use for it here." But he is wrong. His passenger has brought a haiku light as a bog cotton flower. Neither speaks of the return passage.

The engine cuts
to a long glide
and the keel grinds in the sand

Just as he remembers it from his youth, it lies beyond the dunes, in the heart of the little island. There the rusty bog enjoys its brief flowering.

Beside a sky-blue pool
shocked
by their wordless whiteness

Silhouetted on the crag above are the ruins of a hermitage. It is like so many on these *Isles of the Blessed, set in the Western Sea.* Little remains except for a single window, blank to the sky.

"A perfect arch!"
each rough stone
supports the next

He falls to his knees. "Tell me the answer, blustering wind and screaming gulls, quivering bog cotton and rough old stones!" Yet again the wind, the gulls, the bog cotton and the stones all throw back the words in his face.

But finally, as the daylight fades, his question is blown away in the wind, lost in the screams of the gulls, and sinks in the silence of stones. And in his eyes a single warm tear wells up. And the bog cotton? Ah, the dancing bog cotton!

[With grateful acknowledgement to Kenneth White, whose haiku was published in *Handbook for the Diamond Country: Selected Shorter Poems, 1960-90*. Mainstream Publishing, Edinburgh, 1990.]

Haiku

It comes out entire
its black earth shaken free
the good death
of a weed

Fallen apple
a wasp at home
in its hollow heart

Dead fly
I was with it
when it died

Beneath the overflow
a family of spiders
their life

A gentle thud
and miles of grief
at a small life gone

Autumn again
the smooth black stone
stained with rain

Sickle moon
a rabbit's scream
reminds me

Hidden in my wilderness
an ancient way
beside a tinkling stream

Black reef ahead
but in the rigging
the wind is singing